Alien
Adventures

The Rats
of Rolia

Janice Pimm • Jonatronix

OXFORD
UNIVERSITY PRESS

Max's mission log

We are travelling through space on board the micro-ship Excelsa with our new friend, Eight.

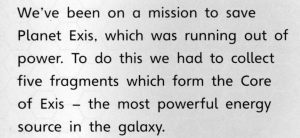

We've been on a mission to save Planet Exis, which was running out of power. To do this we had to collect five fragments which form the Core of Exis – the most powerful energy source in the galaxy.

It's not been easy. A space villain called Badlaw wanted the power of the Core for himself. He and his army of Krools tried to stop us. We eventually defeated Badlaw and he was banished from Planet Exis for 100 years.

Fragments collected: 5

In our last adventure ...

After all our adventures, we were feeling homesick. It was time to leave. As a parting gift, the king and queen of Exis gave us the Excelsa and a new robot, Eight. We finally said goodbye to our friend, Nok, and the other Exians.

As we flew away from Planet Exis, Badlaw started chasing us in his Destroyer! He said that if he can't have Exis, he'll follow us back home and take over Earth instead!

We flew close to a wormhole, hoping that Badlaw would get sucked in. It worked ... but we were sucked in, too! We ended up in the Delta-Zimmer Galaxy. Our only chance of returning home is to get to the Waythroo Wormhole. There's not much time. The wormhole is due to collapse in 5 days, 7 hours and about 42 minutes ...

Chapter 1 – Into the unknown

Zoom! The Excelsa flew onwards into the vast new galaxy. Distant stars shone in unfamiliar patterns. The crew were heading for the Waythroo Wormhole in the hope that it would lead them back home. They only had five days to reach the wormhole before it was due to collapse ... if they didn't make it they would be stuck in space forever.

Ant's control panel flashed a warning. "Er, I think we may have a problem."

Just then, the ship's voice echoed around the bridge, "*System failing. Replace lintum.*"

"What's lintum?" asked Cat.

"A crystal used to power the computers on board the Excelsa," replied Eight, running a storage check. "It must have cracked when we went through the last wormhole."

"So what happens if it stops working?" asked Max.

As if in response, the ship jerked forward and the engines spluttered.

"We will soon have total system failure!" said Eight.

Quickly, Cat checked their location. "We are close to a planet called Grenin. The database says it is rich in precious crystals."

"There's a chance it could have lintum," said Eight.

"Then we need to go there," said Max. "Take us down, Tiger."

Tiger swallowed hard. This would be his first ever landing. Gritting his teeth, he pushed the steering orbs forward.

Jagged hills rose from the planet's brown, rocky surface. Here and there, deep gashes cut into the hillsides.

"Those look like mines!" Ant said excitedly. "We might find some lintum there."

"*We have to land first!*" thought Tiger, aiming for the only flat piece of land he could see. The ship bumped hard on to the stony ground, then came to a stop. He let out a sigh of relief.

Ant and Eight followed Max down the holo-ramp. Cat and Tiger stayed behind to look after the ship.

Max looked around at the sharp, rocky hills that surrounded them. "So, where should we look first, Eight?" he asked.

"As Ant said, the mines could contain some lintum. Let's start there," replied Eight.

Max, Ant and Eight grew to normal size and set off.

Chapter 2 – The rat army

EEEEEEK! A high-pitched squeak echoed around the hills. It was followed by the sound of clanking metal.

On the bridge of the Excelsa, Cat and Tiger froze.

"What was that?" said Cat, shuddering.

"Look!" Out of the viewscreen, Tiger could see two columns of rats marching towards their ship. They had deep red fur and golden armour that glinted brightly in the sun.

"Remember Reeba?" said Tiger. Reeba was a space rat that they had met on a previous adventure. "He was friendly. Maybe these rats will be, too."

"Erm ... I'm not so sure," said Cat, as the rats came closer. "They don't look friendly at all!"

She reached for the cloaking device to hide the ship, but it was too late.

Ear-splitting squeaks filled the air as the rats swarmed around the Excelsa. They circled the micro-ship, their green eyes shining greedily. Then they surged forward, clambering over each other, scraping the sides of the Excelsa with sharp claws.

Inside the Excelsa, Cat screamed as the image of a huge rat filled the viewscreen.

A moment later, the Excelsa started to rock from side to side. Tiger's stomach lurched as the micro-ship was hoisted into the air and the two friends were thrown to the floor. The rats were carrying the Excelsa away!

Chapter 3 – A nasty surprise

Meanwhile, Eight scanned the ground with her crystal detector, shaking her head in frustration. Max and Ant stood by anxiously.

"What happens if we can't find any lintum? Is there another way to fix the ship?" asked Ant.

"I'm afraid not," Eight replied. "We *must* find some!"

ZZZZzzzz! Finally, Eight's computers whirred and her arm flashed. She lifted a large, mottled stone. Underneath it was a tiny piece of white crystal that gleamed in the sunlight.

"Lintum!" cried Eight.

Max sighed with relief as Eight picked up the lintum and put it in her storage unit.

"Right, let's get back to the ship," said Max. He led the way out of the quarry, back the way they had come.

As they reached the top of the ridge, Max stopped abruptly. He motioned for the others to get out of sight. They ducked down and peered into the valley below. With horror, the friends watched an army of rats carrying the Excelsa away.

"Cat! Tiger!" cried Ant.

"Follow them!" said Max. "Let's shrink so we won't be seen."

Max and Ant shrank and activated their holo-boards. Then they zoomed after the rats. Eight flew along behind them.

Keeping a safe distance, they followed the rat army along the valley to a shining, metal building jutting out of the rock.

A door opened and the rats carried the Excelsa inside. Before the friends could follow, the door slammed shut with a heavy clang.

Chapter 4 – Captured!

Cat and Tiger peered out from the Excelsa. They were in an enormous hall with shimmering metal walls. Glowing stones lined the floor. The hall was packed with red rats, all jostling and shoving each other.

A large rat in gleaming armour was seated on a raised platform. When he saw the Excelsa, his lips curled up into a smile.

"That one must be the leader," whispered Cat.

The leader threw back his head and let out a piercing squeal. *"EEEKKKKK!"*

All the rats joined in and the squeaking rose to a feverish pitch. Rats crowded around the Excelsa, lifting it high into the air and rocking it from side to side.

Trembling, Cat and Tiger clamped their hands over their ears.

"We've got to get out of here!" yelled Tiger in panic. "We can't use the holo-ramp. They'll see us."

"We'll have to teleport!" Cat shouted back. "It's the only way."

Buffeted from wall to wall, Cat and Tiger made their way to the teleport deck.

"Erm, I haven't done this before…" said Cat, pressing buttons on the teleport control panel. "I'm hoping we'll land outside the hall, away from the rats."

Cat miscalculated. They landed *inside* the hall … behind the jostling rat pack. Luckily, the rats were focused on the Excelsa. Cat and Tiger began to creep away but, as they did so, one of the rats swished its tail, whipping Tiger's legs.

Tiger froze in terror. He had to clamp a hand over his mouth to stop himself crying out.

Just as the rat spun round, Cat grabbed Tiger and pulled him into a tiny crevice, out of sight. The rat twitched its wiry whiskers and sniffed the air.

Chapter 5 – A question of trust

Max, Ant and Eight crouched on the hillside overlooking the metal building. They were trying to work out a plan to save their friends.

Suddenly Ant heard a faint rustling in a scrubby bush nearby. "What's that?" he asked.

"There's something hiding in there," whispered Max, catching a glimpse of green fur. "Come out, whoever you are!"

A green rat in silver armour scuttled out of the bush.

"Reeba!" cried Ant. The rat looked like the friendly space rat the children had met before.

"Wait a minute," said Max. "It isn't Reeba … although it looks similar."

The rat turned and beckoned for the friends to follow.

"Do you think we can trust him?" asked Max.

"I *think* he is trying to help us," said Eight.

"He seems a thousand times more friendly than those red rats anyway," said Ant.

Max, Ant and Eight followed the rat across the craggy hillside until they came to an opening in the rock.

The rat waved its paw, inviting the micro-friends to enter. Inside was a nest full of green rats – male and female, young and old, babies and grandparents, all squeaking and chattering. The rats fell silent when they entered.

A female rat rose to greet the micro-friends. She started to squeal rapidly.

"I wonder what she's saying," said Max.

"I will try to process their language," Eight said. "One moment." Her computers hummed and buzzed. "Welcome to Grenin," Eight translated. "I am Merta. Your guide is Neeka."

"Ask her what's going on," said Max. "Who are the red rats?"

Chapter 6 – The rat's story

Eight continued translating Merta's words: "We rats of Grenin lived in peace until six moons ago when the red rats of Rolia crashed their spaceship on our planet. Since then they have driven us out of our Great Hall. Every day they steal our food."

The Green Rats of Grenin

Information

silver armour ●●•••••••••••

short, soft green fur

- ▶ Home: Planet Grenin – rich in precious metal and crystals.
- ▶ Work: miners and traders.
- ▶ Food: they exchange crystals for food from other planets.
- ▶ Character: kind and welcoming.

The Red Rats of Rolia

Information

golden armour

long, coarse red fur

▶ Home: Planet Rolia – barren with very few resources.

▶ Work: scavengers and raiders.

▶ Food: they steal food from other planets, including Planet Grenin.

▶ Character: cruel and ruthless.

Merta's squeaks grew softer and her whiskers drooped. "Two moons ago my husband, Reeba, left in his space pod to get help. Since then we have heard nothing."

Ant jumped up. "Tell her we have met her husband! He helped us."

"Yes, and we'll do everything we can to help her in return!" added Max.

Chapter 7 – The wrecked ship

Cat and Tiger backed themselves further into the crevice. Cat looked over her shoulder. It looked like the crevice opened out into a narrow tunnel.

"That could be a way out," whispered Cat.

"What about the ship?" asked Tiger. The red rats were still swarming round it. "We can't leave ... we were supposed to look after it."

"Let's try and find the others, then we can figure out what to do," replied Cat.

The tunnel took Cat and Tiger further underground. It led out on to a narrow, crumbling path that ran alongside a vast ravine.

Down in the ravine, red rats were scurrying to and fro carrying big sheets of metal. Others were throwing metal into hot furnaces. Standing at long benches, yet more rats were hammering pieces of metal into shape.

In the centre of the ravine sat a massive spaceship. It was damaged on one side. Rats were hammering new panels on to the ship but a gaping hole remained.

"Do you think that's why they want the Excelsa? To melt it down for metal?" asked Cat in horror.

"Maybe ... but there's lots of metal around here," said Tiger. "I think they want something else."

Tiger pointed to a group of cross-looking rats standing around a bench. Computer parts and bits of an engine core lay in a jumbled mess in front of them. Wires trailed everywhere like a tangled heap of spaghetti. Every so often one of the rats would grumpily toss a useless part on to the floor.

"I think they want our ship's computer or engine core … or both!" exclaimed Tiger.

Cat spun round as she heard a scuffling noise behind her. "Sssshhhh!" she whispered to Tiger.
Tiger felt his skin crawl. "It must be the rats!" There was nowhere to run.

Chapter 8 – Tiger's plan

"Cat! Tiger!" a familiar voice whispered. With relief Cat saw Max, Ant and Eight hurrying towards them. They were accompanied by a green rat.

"Reeba? Is that you?" asked Tiger.

"It's his friend, Neeka," explained Max. "We've been searching for you everywhere. Come on."

The micro-friends followed the green rat along the path and into a maze of tunnels. Eventually, the rocky walls turned to earth as the rat led them into a network of burrows. On the way, Max, Cat, Ant and Tiger exchanged stories.

"I think the Rolians would leave the planet if they could," said Tiger. "They seem quite desperate to fix their ship … and I think we could help."

When they reached the rest of the green rats, Tiger explained his plan. "We'll offer to fix the Rolians' computer and help mend their ship. I'm sure Ant, Eight and I can manage it. Then the Rolians will leave your planet and return the Excelsa to us."

The rats were doubtful, but they agreed to try.

The micro-friends followed Merta, Neeka and a party of the bravest Grenians to the Great Hall.

The metal door opened with a resounding crash. The rats of Rolia crowded behind their leader.

"Tell them we come in peace and want to help fix their ship," Max said to Eight.

Eight whirred then squeaked. With a nasty sneer, the Rolian leader squeaked back at Eight.

"They don't trust us," said Eight. "He says they have our ship and that's all they need."

The Rolian leader's lips curled back to show his deadly pointed teeth. He gave a low menacing hiss. His hind legs quivered as he got ready to pounce.

"Wait!" cried Max.

The leader hesitated for a moment. Then he squealed and charged towards the friends. His red rats squeaked as one, following close behind him. The green rats scattered in all directions.

The micro-friends stood back-to-back as the rats of Rolia closed in.

Then, out of nowhere, a loud humming noise throbbed around them. Looking up, the friends saw a large metal box spinning towards the surface of the planet.

"What is it?" cried Cat.

"It looks like some kind of space pod," murmured Ant.

The space pod landed. The rats of Rolia lost interest in the micro-friends and turned their attention to the pod.

For a while there was silence, then the door of the space pod sprang open. A small green rat appeared on the exit ramp.

"Reeba! Is that really you this time?" called Ant.

The rat nodded and raised a paw in greeting. Merta crept from behind some rocks to join her husband, squeaking rapidly. Reeba listened, then he turned to address the red rats. Eight translated.

"Rats of Rolia, you should let this robot mend your computer. I lost my space pod in their galaxy and I had to build this one using spare parts. They have excellent technology! I will also give you the energy core that has powered my space pod all the way from the Beta-Prime Galaxy. You will have enough power left to return to your own planet ... but on one condition. You must never come to Planet Grenin again."

The micro-friends held their breath. After what seemed like ages, the Rolian leader nodded.

Several hours later, Ant, Tiger and Eight flew the Excelsa out of the Great Hall.

"Two mended ships!" said Ant happily.

The micro-friends joined the rats of Grenin to watch the Rolians depart. The Rolians' great ship rose from the ravine in a cloud of metal dust and shot high into the air.

Reeba held out a metal box to Max. Max lifted the lid. Inside was a pile of gleaming white lintum.

"It is a present just in case we need any more," said Eight. Then she translated for Reeba.

"I can't thank you enough, my friends," said Reeba. "I would like you to stay longer but I know you must hurry to reach your galaxy. Fly well!"

Later Max said to Eight, "Thanks for your help. We couldn't have managed without you … finding the lintum, translating, fixing the ships. Everything."

"I'm here to be of service," said Eight. "Now, let me calculate. We have lost eight hours, twenty-three minutes and six seconds. We now have only four days to reach the wormhole."

"Can we do it?" asked Cat.

"We must," said Max. "Ant, take us to speed level 6 … and hold on tight!"

Find out what happens next in *Trapped in Time*.